Table of Contents

Glossary

Analogy. A way of comparing things to show how they are similar. For example: nose is to smell as tongue is to taste.

Antonym. A word that means the opposite of another word. For example: in and out.

Classifying. Putting similar things into categories.

Compound Words. When two words are put together to make one. Example: sandbox.

Consonants. Letters that are not vowels (a, e, i, o, u, and sometimes y).

Context. A way to figure out the meaning of a new word by relating it to the other words in the sentence.

Homonyms. Two words that sound the same but have different meanings and are usually spelled differently. Example: write and right.

Inference. Using logic to figure out what is unspoken but evident.

Main Idea. Finding the most important points.

Prefix. A syllable at the beginning of a word that changes its meaning.

Riddles. A puzzling question.

Sequencing. Putting things in logical order.

Suffix. A syllable at the end of a word that changes its meaning.

Syllable. Word divisions. Each syllable has one vowel sound.

Syllabication. Dividing words into parts, each with a vowel sound.

Synonyms. Words that mean the same thing.

Vowels. The letters a, e, i, o, u, and sometimes y.

Vocabulary Building: Same And Opposite

Directions: Using the words in the word box, on the line next to the S, write a synonym (same) for the word. On the line next to the A, write an antonym (opposite). One is done for you.

visible	proud	merry	straight	repair	plain
under	melted	unnecessary	later	new	smooth
embarrassed	gloomy	bent	break	fancy	above
icy	valuable	immediate	old	bumpy	vanish

1. crooked

   S: ___bent___

   A: ___straight___

2. beneath

   S: _____

   A: _____

3. frozen

   S: _____

   A: _____

4. ashamed

   S: _____

   A: _____

5. disappear

   S: _____

   A: _____

6. instant

   S: _____

   A: _____

7. cheerful

   S: _____

   A: _____

8. ancient

   S: _____

   A: _____

9. damage

   S: _____

   A: _____

10. elegant

    S: _____

    A: _____

11. important

    S: _____

    A: _____

12. rough

    S: _____

    A: _____

Name: _____

Vocabulary Building: Words That Sound Alike

Directions: Following each sentence are two words. Some are homonyms and some sound very similar. Choose the right word to complete each sentence. One is done for you.

1. The scientist was working on an_____experiment_____ . (experience, experiment)

2. Going to the park is an enjoyable _____ . (experiment, experience)

3. Jimmy was so _____ that he fell asleep. (board, bored)

4. We'll need a _____ and some nails to repair the fence. (board, bored)

5. Do you want _____ after dinner? (desert, dessert)

6. A _____is hot and sandy. (desert, dessert)

7. The soldier had a _____pinned to his uniform. (medal, metal)

8. Gold is a precious _____ . (medal, metal)

9. Which book _____ you want to read first? (do, due)

10. She came to the costume party dressed as a _____ . (bear, bare)

11. Don't _____ at your present before Christmas! (peak, peek)

12. They climbed to the _____ of the mountain. (peak, peek)

13. Jack had to repair the emergency _____ on his car. (brake, break)

14. Please be careful not to _____ my bicycle. (brake, break)

15. The race _____ was a very difficult one. (coarse, course)

16. We will need some _____ sandpaper to finish this job. (coarse, course)

Name: _____

Vocabulary Building: Changing The Meaning Of Words

Directions: Read the list of prefixes and their meanings. Then add a prefix to the beginning of each word in the Word Box to make a word with the meaning given in each sentence below. One is done for you.

PREFIX	MEANING
bi-	two or twice
en-	to make
in-	within
mis-	wrong
non-	not or without
pre-	before
re-	again
un-	not

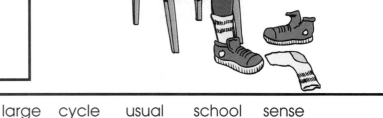

| grown | write | information | large | cycle | usual | school | sense |

1. Jimmy's foot hurt because his toenail was (growing within). _____ingrown_____

2. If you want to see what is in the background, you will have to (make bigger) the photograph. _____

3. I didn't do a very good job on my homework, so I will have to (write it again) it. _____

4. The newspaper article about the event has some (wrong facts). _____

5. I hope I get a (vehicle with two wheels) for my birthday. _____

6. The story he told was complete (words without meaning)! _____

7. Did you go to a (school that comes before usual school age) before you went to kindergarten? _____

8. Her ability to read words upside-down is most (not usual). _____

Name: _____

Vocabulary Building: Make New Words

Directions: Read the list of suffixes and their meanings. Then add a suffix to the end of each word in the word box to make a word with the meaning given in each sentence below. One is done for you.

Remember: In most cases, when adding a suffix that starts with a vowel, drop the final **e** of the root word. For example, fame becomes famous. Also, change a final **y** in the root word to **i** before adding any suffix except -ing. For example, silly becomes silliness.

SUFFIX	MEANING
-ful	full of
-ity	quality or degree
-ive	have or tend to be
-less	without or lacking
-able	able to be
-ness	state of
-ment	act of
-or	person that does something
-ward	in the direction of

effect	like	thought	pay	beauty	real	back	act	happy

1. Mike was grateful for the (the quality of being real) of a hot meal.   *reality*

2. I was (without thinking) for forgetting your birthday. _____

3. The mouse trap we put out doesn't seem to be (have an effect). _____

4. In spring, the flower garden is (full of beauty). _____

5. Sally is such a (able to be liked) girl! _____

6. Tim fell over (in the direction of the back) because he wasn't watching where he was going. _____

7. Jill's wedding day was one of great (the state of being happy). _____

8. The (person who performs) was very good in the last scene of the play. _____

9. I will have to make a (an act of paying) for the stereo that I bought. _____

Name: _____

Vocabulary Building: Context Clues

Where the northern shores of North America meet the Arctic Ocean, the winters are very long and cold. No plants or crops will grow there. This is the land of the <u>Eskimo</u>.

Eskimos have figured out ways to live in the snow and ice. They sometimes live in <u>igloos</u>, which are made of snow. It is really very comfortable inside! An oil lamp provides light and warmth.

Often, you will find a big, furry <u>husky</u> sleeping in the long tunnel that leads to the igloo. Huskies are very important to Eskimos because they pull their sleds and help with hunting. Eskimos are excellent hunters.

Many, many years ago they learned to make <u>harpoons</u> and spears to help them hunt their food.

Eskimos get much of their food from the sea, especially fish, seals,and whales. Often, an Eskimo will go out in a <u>kayak</u> to fish. Only one Eskimo fits inside, and he drives it with a paddle. High waves may turn the kayak upside down, but the Eskimo does not fall out. He is so skillful with a paddle that he quickly is right side up again.

Directions: After reading the paragraphs, write each underlined word in its definition at the bottom of the page.

A _____ is a large, strong dog.

An _____ is a member of the race of people who live on the Arctic coasts of North America and in parts of Greenland.

An _____ is a house made of packed snow.

A _____ is a one-person canoe made of animal skins.

A _____ is a spear with a long rope attached. It is used for spearing whales and other large sea animals.

Name: _____

Vocabulary Building: People And Their Jobs

Directions: Unscramble the underlined words to tell the title of the person who does the job described. One is done for you.

1. A <u>inacimus</u> writes, sings, or plays music.   musician

2. An <u>trasotanu</u> is trained to fly a spaceship. _____

3. An <u>itrode</u> prepares other people's writing to be printed in a book, newspaper, or magazine. _____

4. An <u>rigeenen</u> operates an engine, such as on a train _____

5. An <u>brocata</u> performs gymmastic or tumbling exercises that use control of the body. _____

6. A <u>ilaort</u> makes clothing for people. _____

7. A <u>veecitted</u> works to get information, especially about crimes or suspicious people. _____

8. A <u>tissicent</u> works and performs experiments in one of the sciences, such as chemistry. _____

9. An <u>sattir</u> makes such beautiful things as paintings and statues. _____

10. A <u>hocca</u> teaches and trains students, especially in sports. _____

11. An <u>rotac</u> performs in plays or movies. _____

12. A <u>suner</u> is trained to care for sick people and to assist doctors. _____

13. A <u>naicigam</u> is a performer skilled in magic tricks. _____

Name: _____

Review

Directions: Work the puzzle to review the words you have learned.

Across

2. An antonym for fancy.
3. A person who solves crimes.
7. A one-person canoe used by Eskimos.
9. A person who cares for sick people and assists doctors.
11. A homonym for board.
12. A synonym for disappear.
13. This pumps blood with every beat.

Down

1. An antonym for old.
2. A homonym for peak.
4. A root word plus a suffix that means "without care."
5. A snow house some Eskimos live in.
6. You think with this.
8. A person who performs in a movie or play.
10. A prefix plus a root word that means "read again."

Following Directions: People And Their Jobs

Directions: Find each word from the word box in the puzzle and draw a circle around it. Some words go across, some go down. One word is diagonal and one is written backwards. The first word is done for you.

m	a	g	i	c	i	a	n	d	o	a	s
u	a	r	m	p	v	c	u	e	j	a	c
s	p	y	g	t	o	t	r	t	n	p	i
i	l	s	t	b	k	o	s	e	r	a	e
c	o	a	c	h	e	r	e	c	e	s	n
i	u	l	t	m	d	t	n	t	d	t	t
a	c	r	o	b	a	t	g	i	i	r	i
n	k	t	v	i	o	j	i	v	t	o	s
o	p	n	l	t	t	r	n	e	o	n	t
a	b	o	i	i	c	i	e	d	r	a	n
c	r	d	d	m	p	e	e	f	t	u	a
p	e	e	t	s	i	t	r	a	r	t	j

magician
scientist
coach
astronaut
musician
acrobat
tailor
engineer
nurse
detective
actor
artist
editor

Directions: Draw a line between each job and the word that best goes with it.

actor	wand
tailor	basketball
acrobat	painting
astronaut	guitar
coach	medicine
editor	telescope
scientist	stage
magician	mystery
artist	somersault
nurse	scissors
engineer	rocket
musician	locomotive
detective	newspaper

Name: _____

Following Directions: Reading A Map

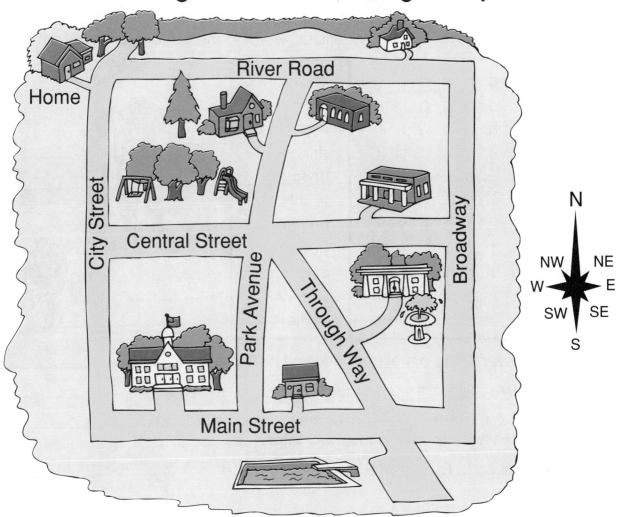

Directions: Follow the directions written below to reach a "mystery" location on the map.

1. Begin at Home.
2. Drive east on River Road.
3. Turn south on Broadway.
4. Drive to Central Street and turn west.
5. When you get to City Street, turn south.
6. Turn east on Main Street and drive one block to Park Avenue, turn north.
7. At Central Street turn east, then turn southeast on Through Way.
8. Drive to the end of Through Way. Your "mystery" location is to the west.

You are at the _____ .

That was a long drive to get there. What is an easier way to get back home?

Name: _____

Following Directions: Sports Puzzle

Directions: All of the words in the word box have something to do with sports. Find each word in the puzzle, then unscramble the underlined words in the sentences below.

v	k	r	v	c	o	a	c	h	g
b	m	d	i	a	m	o	n	d	u
t	o	u	c	h	d	o	w	n	n
s	n	m	t	e	c	l	u	b	i
e	d	p	o	l	d	v	i	c	f
b	m	i	r	m	g	i	r	t	o
o	e	r	y	e	s	c	e	y	r
o	t	e	s	t	r	i	k	e	m
t	c	h	a	m	p	i	o	n	r
y	r	a	c	k	e	t	e	y	m

champion
helmet
diamond
strike
uniform
touchdown
umpire
coach
club
victory
racket

1. A football player wears a <u>melteh</u> to protect his head. _____

2. If our team wins tonight, it will be their tenth <u>rticoyv</u> this year. _____

3. When it rained, they put a cover over the baseball <u>middona</u> so we wouldn't have to play in the mud later. _____

4. Our <u>hacco</u> asked us to stay after school to practice for the game. _____

5. With only a minute left in the football game, Jimmy scored the winning <u>wontcudoh</u>. _____

6. In golf, you hit the ball with a <u>bluc</u>. _____

7. Do all boxing fans know the name of the heavyweight <u>miocpahn</u>? _____

8. I thought I tagged the base, but the <u>mipure</u> said I was out. _____

9. In tennis, you hit the ball with a <u>rcatek</u>. _____

10. If we earn enough money selling candy, our team will get new <u>nifmorus</u>. _____

11. I bet our best pitcher can <u>trekis</u> out your best hitter. _____

Name: _____

Following Directions: The Planets

Directions: Read about the planets. Then unscramble the name of each planet and write it on the line.

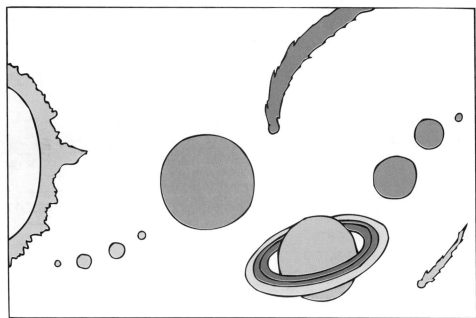

1. Neptune takes 165 years to complete its path, or orbit, around the sun.
2. Jupiter has 16 moons orbiting around it.
3. Pluto is the coldest planet, with temperatures close to 400 degrees below zero!
4. Mars is nicknamed the Red Planet.
5. Saturn is one of the most beautiful planets to look at through a telescope because of the many rings that surround it.
6. Mercury is the planet closest to the sun.
7. Earth is the planet we live on. It is sometimes called the Life Planet.
8. Until recent discoveries, Venus was thought of as the "mystery planet" because it is covered by thick clouds.
9. Uranus is different from the other planets because it is lying on its side.

rUsanu _____   rathE _____

sarM _____   seVun _____

peNnute _____   aruntS _____

cryMure _____   oPult _____

piteJur _____

Name: _____

Sequencing: Recipe For Brownies

Directions: Read the recipe. Then number in order the steps for making brownies.

Preheat the oven to 350 degrees. Grease an 8-inch square baking dish.

In a mixing bowl, put 2 squares (2 ounces) of unsweetened chocolate and 1/3 cup of butter. Put the bowl in a pan of hot water and heat it to melt the chocolate and butter.

When the chocolate is melted, remove the pan from the heat. Add one cup of sugar and two eggs to the melted chocolate and beat it. Next, stir in 3/4 cup of sifted flour, 1/2 teaspoon of baking powder, and 1/2 teaspoon salt. Finally, mix in 1/2 cup of chopped nuts.

Spread the mixture in the greased baking dish. Bake for 30 to 35 minutes. The brownies are finished baking when a toothpick stuck in the center comes out clean. Let the brownies cool. Cut them into squares.

Directions: Number in order the steps for making brownies.

_____ Stick a toothpick in the center of the brownies to be sure they are finished.

_____ Mix in chopped nuts.

_____ Melt chocolate and butter in a mixing bowl over a pan of hot water.

_____ Cool brownies and cut in squares.

_____ Beat in sugar and eggs.

_____ Spread mixture in baking dish.

_____ Stir in flour, baking powder, and salt.

_____ Bake for 30 to 35 minutes.

_____ Turn oven to 350 degrees and grease pan.

Name: _____

Sequencing: Change Salt Into Pepper!

Imagine doing this trick for your friends. You pick up a salt shaker that everyone can see is full of salt. Pour some into your hand. You tell your audience that you will change the salt into pepper. You say a few magic words, such as "Fibbiddy, dibbiddy, milkshake and malt. What will be pepper once was salt!" Then you open your hand and pour out pepper!

How is it done? First you will need a clear salt shaker with a screw-on top. You also will need a paper napkin and a small amount of pepper.

Take off the top of the salt shaker. Lay the napkin over the opening, and push it down a little to make a small pocket. Fill the pocket with pepper. Put the top back on the salt shaker and tear off the extra napkin. Now you are ready for the trick.

Hold up the salt shaker so your audience can see that it is full of salt. Shake some "salt" into your hand. Close your fist so no one can see that it is really pepper. Say the magic words and open your hand.

Directions: After reading how to do a magic trick that will amaze your friends, number in order the steps to do the trick.

_____ Say some magic words.

_____ Find a clear salt shaker with a screw-on top.

_____ Open your hand and pour out the pepper.

_____ Take off the top of the salt shaker.

_____ Show the audience the shaker full of salt.

_____ Place the napkin over the opening of the salt shaker.

_____ Get a paper napkin and some pepper.

_____ Put the pepper in the napkin "pocket."

_____ Shake some "salt" into your hand and close your fist.

_____ Put the top back on the salt shaker and tear off the extra napkin.

Name: _____

Sequencing: From Tadpole To Frog

Frogs and toads belong to a group of animals called amphibians (am-FIB-ee-ans). This big word means "living a double life." Frogs and toads live a "double life" because they live part of their lives in water and part on land. They are able to do this because their bodies change as they grow. This series of changes is called metamorphosis (met-a-MORE-fa-sis).

A mother frog lays her eggs in water and then leaves them on their own to grow. The eggs contain cells — the tiny "building blocks" of all living things — that multiply and grow. Soon the cells grow into a swimming tadpole. Tadpoles breathe through gills — small holes in their sides — like fish do. They spend all of their time in the water.

The tadpole changes as it grows. Back legs slowly form. Front legs begin inside the tadpole under the gill holes. They pop out when they are fully developed. At the same time, lungs, which a frog uses to breathe instead of gills, are almost ready to be used.

As the tadpole reaches the last days of its life in the water, its tail seems to disappear. When all of the tadpole's body parts are ready for life on land, it has become a frog.

Directions: After reading how a tadpole changes into a frog, number in order the stages it went through.

_____   The front legs pop out. The lungs are ready to use for breathing.

_____   The cells in the egg multiply and grow.

_____   The tadpole has become a frog.

_____   Back legs slowly form.

_____   Soon the cells grow into a swimming tadpole.

_____   Front legs develop inside the tadpole.

_____   The tadpole's tail seems to disappear.

_____   A mother frog lays her eggs in water.

ANSWER KEY

This Answer Key has been designed so that it may be easily removed if you so desire.

GRADE 4 READING

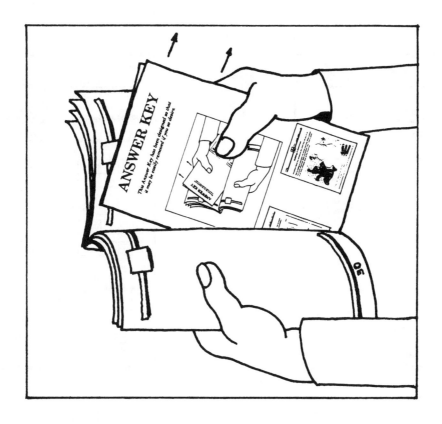

Same And Opposite

Directions: Using the words in the word box, on the line next to the S, write a synonym (same) for the word. On the line next to the A, write an antonym (opposite). One is done for you.

visible	proud	merry	straight	repair	plain
under	melted	unnecessary	later	new	smooth
embarrassed	gloomy	bent	break	fancy	above
icy	valuable	immediate	old	bumpy	vanish

1. crooked
   S: bent
   A: straight

2. beneath
   S: under
   A: above

3. frozen
   S: icy
   A: melted

4. ashamed
   S: embarrassed
   A: proud

5. disappear
   S: vanish
   A: visible

6. instant
   S: immediate
   A: later

7. cheerful
   S: merry
   A: gloomy

8. ancient
   S: old
   A: new

9. damage
   S: break
   A: repair

10. elegant
    S: fancy
    A: plain

11. important
    S: valuable
    A: unnecessary

12. rough
    S: bumpy
    A: smooth

Copyright © 1991 American Education Publishing Co.

3

Words That Sound Alike Or Similar

Directions: Following each sentence are two words. Some are homonyms and some sound very similar. Choose the right word to complete each sentence. One is done for you.

1. The scientist was working on an **experiment**. (experience, experiment)

2. Going to the park is an enjoyable **experience**. (experiment, experience)

3. Jimmy was so **bored** that he fell asleep. (board, bored)

4. We'll need a **board** and some nails to repair the fence. (board, bored)

5. Do you want **dessert** after dinner? (desert, dessert)

6. A **desert** is hot and sandy. (desert, dessert)

7. The soldier had a **medal** pinned to his uniform. (medal, metal)

8. Gold is a precious **metal**. (medal, metal)

9. Which book **do** you want to read first? (do, due)

10. She came to the costume party dressed as a **bear**. (bear, bare)

11. Don't **peek** at your present before Christmas! (peak, peek)

12. They climbed to the **peak** of the mountain. (peak, peek)

13. Jack had to repair the emergency **brake** on his car. (brake, break)

14. Please be careful not to **break** my bicycle. (brake, break)

15. The race **course** was a very difficult one. (coarse, course)

16. We will need some **coarse** sandpaper to finish this job. (coarse, course)

Copyright © 1991 American Education Publishing Co.

4

Name: _____

Changing The Meaning Of Words

Directions: Read the list of prefixes and their meanings. Then add a prefix to the beginning of each word in the Word Box to make a word with the meaning given in each sentence below. One is done for you.

PREFIX	MEANING
bi-	two or twice
en-	to make
in-	within
mis-	wrong
non-	not or without
pre-	before
re-	again
un-	not

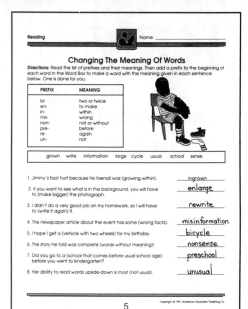

| grown | write | information | large | cycle | usual | school | sense |

1. Jimmy's foot hurt because his toenail was (growing within). **ingrown**

2. If you want to see what is in the background, you will have to (make bigger) the photograph. **enlarge**

3. I didn't do a very good job on my homework, so I will have to (write it again) it. **rewrite**

4. The newspaper article about the event has some (wrong facts). **misinformation**

5. I hope I get a (vehicle with two wheels) for my birthday. **bicycle**

6. The story he told was complete (words without meaning)! **nonsense**

7. Did you go to a (school that comes before usual school age) before you went to kindergarten? **preschool**

8. Her ability to read words upside-down is most (not usual). **unusual**

Name: _____

People And Their Jobs

Directions: Unscramble the underlined words to tell the title of the person who does the job described. One is done for you.

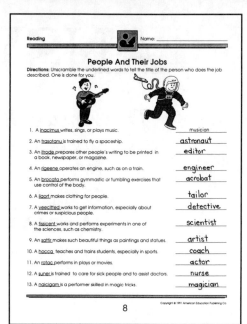

1. A <u>inacimus</u> writes, sings, or plays music. musician

2. An <u>trasotanu</u> is trained to fly a spaceship. **astronaut**

3. An <u>itrode</u> prepares other people's writing to be printed in a book, newspaper, or magazine. **editor**

4. An <u>rigeene</u> operates an engine, such as on a train. **engineer**

5. An <u>brocata</u> performs gymnastic or tumbling exercises that use control of the body. **acrobat**

6. A <u>liaort</u> makes clothing for people. **tailor**

7. A <u>veecittid</u> works to get information, especially about crimes or suspicious people. **detective**

8. A <u>fissicent</u> works and performs experiments in one of the sciences, such as chemistry. **scientist**

9. An <u>sattir</u> makes such beautiful things as paintings and statues. **artist**

10. A <u>hocca</u> teaches and trains students, especially in sports. **coach**

11. An <u>rotac</u> performs in plays or movies. **actor**

12. A <u>suner</u> is trained to care for sick people and to assist doctors. **nurse**

13. A <u>naicigam</u> is a performer skilled in magic tricks. **magician**

Name: _____

Make New Words

Directions: Read the list of suffixes and their meanings. Then add a suffix to the end of each word in the word box to make a word with the meaning given in each sentence below. One is done for you.

Remember: In most cases, when adding a suffix that starts with a vowel, drop the final **e** of the root word. For example, fame becomes famous. Also, change a final **y** in the root word to **i** before adding any suffix except -ing. For example, silly becomes silliness.

SUFFIX	MEANING
-ful	full of
-ity	quality or degree
-ive	have or tend to be
-less	without or lacking
-able	able to be
-ness	state of
-ment	act of
-or	person that does something
-ward	in the direction of

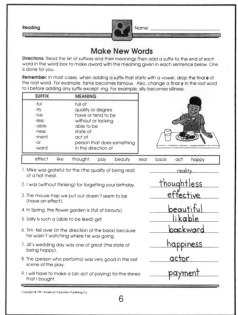

| effect | like | thought | pay | beauty | real | back | act | happy |

1. Mike was grateful for the (the quality of being real) of a hot meal. **reality**

2. I was (without thinking) for forgetting your birthday. **thoughtless**

3. The mouse trap we put out doesn't seem to be (have an effect). **effective**

4. In Spring, the flower garden is (full of beauty). **beautiful**

5. Sally is such a (able to be liked) girl! **likable**

6. Tim fell over (in the direction of the back) because he wasn't watching where he was going. **backward**

7. Jill's wedding day was one of great (the state of being happy). **happiness**

8. The (person who performs) was very good in the last scene of the play. **actor**

9. I will have to make a (an act of paying) for the stereo that I bought. **payment**

Name: _____

Review

Directions: Work the puzzle to review the words you have learned.

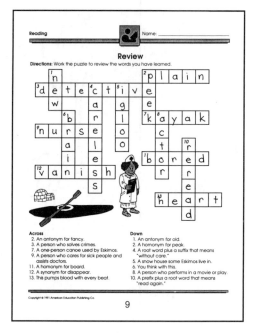

Across

2. An antonym for fancy.
3. A person who solves crimes.
7. A one-person canoe used by Eskimos.
9. A person who cares for sick people and assists doctors.
11. A homonym for board.
12. A synonym for disappear.
13. This pumps blood with every beat.

Down

1. An antonym for old.
2. A homonym for peak.
4. A root word plus a suffix that means "without care."
5. A snow house some Eskimos live in.
6. You think with this.
8. A person who performs in a movie or play.
10. A prefix plus a root word that means "read again."

Name: _____

Eskimos

Where the northern shores of North American meet the Arctic Ocean, the winters are very long and cold. No plants or crops will grow there. This is the land of the <u>Eskimo</u>.

Eskimos have figured out ways to live in the snow and ice. They sometimes live in <u>igloos</u>, which are made of snow and ice. It is really very comfortable inside! An oil lamp provides light and warmth.

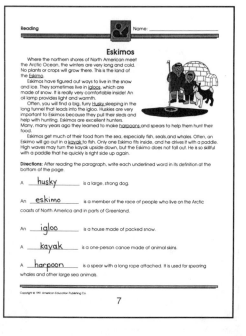

Often, you will find a big, furry <u>Husky</u> sleeping in the long tunnel that leads into the igloo. Huskies are very important to Eskimos because they pull their sleds and help with hunting. Eskimos are excellent hunters. Many, many years ago they learned to make <u>harpoons</u> and spears to help them hunt their food.

Eskimos get much of their food from the sea, especially fish, seals, and whales. Often, an Eskimo will go out in a <u>kayak</u> to fish. Only one Eskimo fits inside, and he drives it with a paddle. High waves may turn the kayak upside down, but the Eskimo does not fall out. He is so skillful with a paddle that he quickly is right side up again.

Directions: After reading the paragraph, write each underlined word in its definition at the bottom of the page.

A ___**husky**___ is a large, strong dog.

An ___**eskimo**___ is a member of the race of people who live on the Arctic coasts of North America and in parts of Greenland.

An ___**igloo**___ is a house made of packed snow.

A ___**kayak**___ is a one-person canoe made of animal skins.

A ___**harpoon**___ is a spear with a long rope attached. It is used for spearing whales and other large sea animals.

Name: _____

People And Their Jobs

Directions: Find each word from the word box in the puzzle and draw a circle around it. Some words go across, some go down. One word is diagonal and one is written backwards. The first word is done for you.

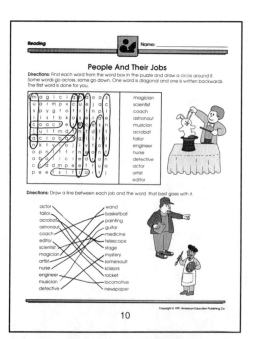

| magician |
| scientist |
| coach |
| astronaut |
| musician |
| acrobat |
| tailor |
| engineer |
| nurse |
| detective |
| actor |
| artist |
| editor |

Directions: Draw a line between each job and the word that best goes with it.

actor	wand
tailor	basketball
acrobat	painting
astronaut	guitar
coach	medicine
editor	telescope
scientist	stage
magician	mystery
artist	somersault
nurse	scissors
engineer	rocket
musician	locomotive
detective	newspaper

Reading A Map

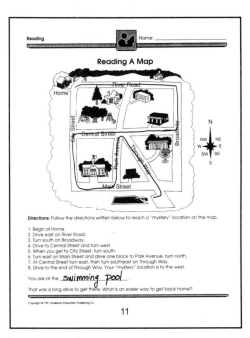

Directions: Follow the directions written below to reach a "mystery" location on the map.

1. Begin at Home.
2. Drive east on River Road.
3. Turn south on Broadway.
4. Drive to Central Street and turn west.
5. When you get to City Street, turn south.
6. Turn east on Main Street and drive one block to Park Avenue, turn north.
7. At Central Street turn east, then turn southeast on Through Way.
8. Drive to the end of Through Way. Your "mystery" location is to the west.

You are at the <u>Swimming Pool</u>.

That was a long drive to get there. What is an easier way to get back home?

Sports Puzzle

Directions: All of the words in the word box have something to do with sports. Find each word in the puzzle, then unscramble the underlined words in the sentences below.

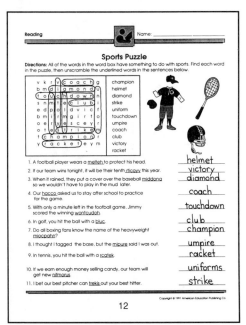

champion
helmet
diamond
strike
uniform
touchdown
umpire
coach
club
victory
racket

1. A football player wears a <u>melteh</u> to protect his head.
2. If our team wins tonight, it will be their tenth <u>rticovy</u> this year.
3. When it rained, they put a cover over the baseball <u>middona</u> so we wouldn't have to play in the mud later.
4. Our <u>hacoc</u> asked us to stay after school to practice for the game.
5. With only a minute left in the football game, Jimmy scored the winning <u>wontcudoh</u>.
6. In golf, you hit the ball with a <u>bluc</u>.
7. Do all boxing fans know the name of the heavyweight <u>miocpohn</u>?
8. I thought I tagged the base, but the <u>mipure</u> said I was out.
9. In tennis, you hit the ball with a <u>rcatek</u>.
10. If we earn enough money selling candy, our team will get new <u>nrfmorus</u>.
11. I bet our best pitcher can <u>trekis</u> out your best hitter.

helmet
victory
diamond
coach
touchdown
club
champion
umpire
racket
uniforms
strike

The Planets

Directions: Read about the planets. Then unscramble the name of each planet and write it on the line.

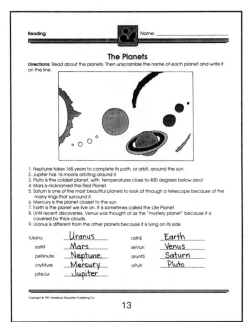

1. Neptune takes 165 years to complete its path, or orbit, around the sun.
2. Jupiter has 16 moons orbiting around it.
3. Pluto is the coldest planet, with temperatures close to 400 degrees below zero!
4. Mars is nicknamed the Red Planet.
5. Saturn is one of the most beautiful planets to look at through a telescope because of the many rings that surround it.
6. Mercury is the planet closest to the sun.
7. Earth is the planet we live on. It is sometimes called the Life Planet.
8. Until recent discoveries, Venus was thought of as the "mystery planet" because it is covered by thick clouds.
9. Uranus is different from the other planets because it is lying on its side.

rUsanu	<u>Uranus</u>	rathE	<u>Earth</u>
sarM	<u>Mars</u>	seVun	<u>Venus</u>
peNnute	<u>Neptune</u>	aruntS	<u>Saturn</u>
cryMure	<u>Mercury</u>	oPult	<u>Pluto</u>
piteJur	<u>Jupiter</u>		

Recipe For Brownies

Directions: Read the recipe. Then number in order the steps for making brownies.

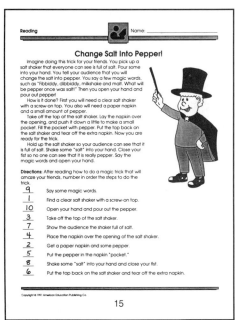

Preheat the oven to 350 degrees. Grease an 8-inch square baking dish.

In a mixing bowl, put 2 squares (2 ounces) of unsweetened chocolate and 1/3 cup of butter. Put the bowl in a pan of hot water and heat it to melt the chocolate.

When the chocolate is melted, remove the pan from the heat. Add one cup of sugar and two eggs to the melted chocolate and beat it. Next, stir in 3/4 cup of sifted flour, 1/2 teaspoon of baking powder, and 1/2 teaspoon salt. Finally, mix in 1/2 cup of chopped nuts.

Spread the mixture in the greased baking dish. Bake for 30 to 35 minutes. The brownies are finished baking when a toothpick stuck in the center comes out clean. Let the brownies cool. Cut them into squares.

Directions: Number in order the steps for making brownies.

  8   Stick a toothpick in the center of the brownies to be sure they are finished.
  5   Mix in chopped nuts.
  2   Melt chocolate and butter in a mixing bowl over a pan of hot water.
  9   Cool brownies and cut in squares.
  3   Beat in sugar and eggs.
  6   Spread mixture in baking dish.
  4   Stir in flour, baking powder, and salt.
  7   Bake for 30 to 35 minutes.
  1   Turn oven to 350 degrees and grease pan.

Change Salt Into Pepper!

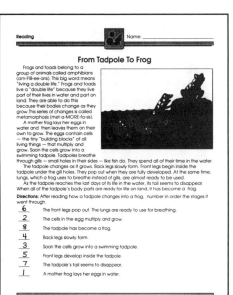

Imagine doing this trick for your friends. You pick up a salt shaker that everyone can see is full of salt. Pour some into your hand. You tell your audience that you will change the salt into pepper. You say a few magic words, such as "Fibbidy, dibbidy, milkshake and malt. What will be pepper once was salt!" Then you open your hand and pour out pepper!

How is it done? First you will need a clear salt shaker with a screw-on top. You also will need a paper napkin and a small amount of pepper.

Take off the top of the salt shaker. Lay the napkin over the opening, and push it down a little to make a small pocket. Fill the pocket with pepper. Put the top back on the salt shaker and tear off the extra napkin. Now you are ready for the trick.

Hold up the salt shaker so your audience can see that it is full of salt. Shake some "salt" into your hand. Close your fist so no one can see that it is really pepper. Say the magic words and open your hand.

Directions: After reading how to do a magic trick that will amaze your friends, number in order the steps to do the trick.

  9   Say some magic words.
  1   Find a clear salt shaker with a screw-on top.
 10   Open your hand and pour out the pepper.
  3   Take off the top of the salt shaker.
  7   Show the audience the shaker full of salt.
  4   Place the napkin over the opening of the salt shaker.
  2   Get a paper napkin and some pepper.
  5   Put the pepper in the napkin "pocket."
  8   Shake some "salt" into your hand and close your fist.
  6   Put the top back on the salt shaker and tear off the extra napkin.

From Tadpole To Frog

Frogs and toads belong to a group of animals called amphibians (am-FIB-ee-ans). This big word means "living a double life." Frogs and toads live a "double life" because they live part of their lives in water and part on land. They are able to do this because their bodies change as they grow. This series of changes is called metamorphosis (met-a-MORE-fa-sis).

A mother frog lays her eggs in water and then leaves them on their own to grow. The eggs contain cells — the tiny "building blocks" of all living things — that multiply and grow. Soon the cells grow into a swimming tadpole. Tadpoles breathe through gills — small holes in their sides — like fish do. They spend all of their time in the water.

The tadpole changes as it grows. Back legs slowly form. At the same time, front legs begin inside the gill holes. They pop out when they are fully developed. At the same time, lungs, which a frog uses to breathe instead of gills, are almost ready to be used.

As the tadpole reaches the last days of its life in the water, its tail seems to disappear. When all of the tadpole's body parts are ready for life on land, it has become a frog.

Directions: After reading how a tadpole changes into a frog, number in order the stages that it went through.

  6   The front legs pop out. The lungs are ready to use for breathing.
  2   The cells in the egg multiply and grow.
  8   The tadpole has become a frog.
  4   Back legs slowly form.
  3   Soon the cells grow into a swimming tadpole.
  5   Front legs develop inside the tadpole.
  7   The tadpole's tail seems to disappear.
  1   A mother frog lays her eggs in water.

Review

Here's a science experiment that you can do in your own backyard. To make this "rocket launcher," you will need an empty one-quart soda bottle, a cork, a paper towel, a half cup of water, a half cup of vinegar, and one teaspoon of baking soda. You may want to add some streamers.

The cork will be the "rocket." If you attach tissue-paper streamers to the cork with a thumbtack, you will be able to more easily follow the rocket during its flight.

— Pour the water and vinegar into the "launcher" — the bottle. Cut the paper towel into a four-inch square. Put the baking soda into the middle of the paper towel. Roll up the towel and twist the ends so the baking soda will stay inside.

Outside, where there will be plenty of room for your rocket to fly, drop the paper towel and the baking soda into the bottle. Put the cork on as tightly as you can.

The liquid will soak through the paper towel. This lets the baking soda and vinegar work together to make a kind of gas called carbon dioxide. As the carbon dioxide builds up in the bottle, it will push out the cork. Soon the cork will shoot up to the sky with a loud pop!

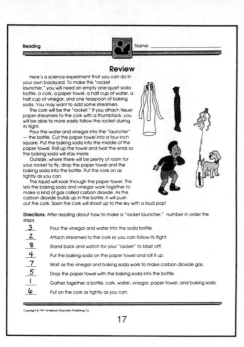

Directions: After reading about how to make a "rocket launcher," number in order the steps.

- 3 Pour the vinegar and water into the soda bottle.
- 2 Attach streamers to the cork so you can follow its flight.
- 8 Stand back and watch for your "rocket" to blast off!
- 4 Put the baking soda on the paper towel and roll it up.
- 7 Wait as the vinegar and baking soda work to make carbon dioxide gas.
- 5 Drop the paper towel with the baking soda into the bottle.
- 1 Gather together a bottle, cork, water, vinegar, paper towel, and baking soda.
- 6 Put on the cork as tightly as you can.

Relating Things

Directions: Write a word from the word box to complete the following analogies. One is done for you.

cut	carry	ran	arm	listen
paint	lie	children	fifty	out
puppy	summer	hot	water	egg

1. Pencil is to write as brush is to — paint
2. Foot is to leg as hand is to — arm
3. Crayons are to draw as scissors are to — cut
4. Leg is to walk as arm is to — carry
5. Baby is to babies as child is to — children
6. Eye is to look as ear is to — listen
7. Chair is to sit as bed is to — lie
8. 600 is to 300 as 100 is to — fifty
9. White is to black as in is to — out
10. Ice skate is to winter as swim is to — summer
11. Switch is to light as faucet is to — water
12. Fly is to flew as run is to — ran
13. Cow is to milk as chicken is to — egg
14. Cool is to cold as warm is to — hot
15. Cat is to kitten as dog is to — puppy

Which One Does Not Belong?

Directions: For each one, cross out the word that does not belong with the others.

1. Cross out the word that is not a building.
   factory   hotel   lodge   ~~pattern~~
2. Cross out the word that is not a month.
   ~~Thursday~~   September   December   October
3. Cross out the word that is not a place where people live.
   cottage   hut   ~~carpenter~~   castle
4. Cross out the word that is not found in a kitchen.
   cupboard   ~~orchard~~   refrigerator   stove
5. Cross out the word that is not a holiday.
   Christmas   Thanksgiving   Easter   ~~Spring~~
6. Cross out the word that is not a kind of metal.
   brass   copper   ~~coal~~   tin
7. Cross out the word that is not a part of the body.
   stomach   ~~breathe~~   liver   brain
8. Cross out the word that is not a person.
   teacher   mother   dentist   ~~office~~
9. Cross out the word that is not found in a bathroom.
   ~~mirror~~   faucet   bathtub   sink
10. Cross out the word that is not an area of a house.
   basement   attic   kitchen   ~~neighborhood~~

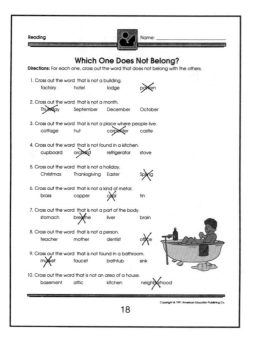

What Fits Best?

Directions: For each analogy, write a word from the word box that best fits.

fence	club	glove	saw	father
blanket	dish	rug	snow	ten
compass	hat	brake	finger	blue

1. Racket is to tennis as club is to golf.
2. Glass is to drink as dish is to eat.
3. Wheel is to steer as brake is to stop.
4. Roof is to house as rug is to floor.
5. Rain is to storm as snow is to blizzard.
6. Clock is to time as compass is to directions.
7. Lid is to pan as hat is to head.
8. Hammer is to pound as saw is to cut.
9. Mother is to daughter as father is to son.
10. Shoe is to foot as glove is to hand.
11. Five is to ten as ten is to twenty.
12. Shade is to lamp as blanket is to bed.
13. Toe is to foot as finger is to hand.
14. Frame is to picture as fence is to yard.
15. Green is to grass as blue is to sky.

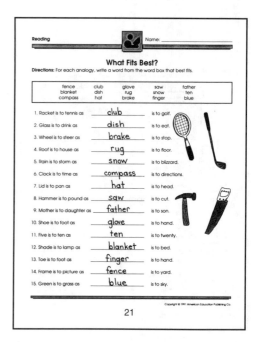

The Five Senses

Directions: Each of the words in the word box makes you think of hearing, seeing, smelling, tasting, or touching. Write each word under the sense that is used. One is done for you.

music	rainbow	talking	hot	sour
honking	moldy	butterfly	green	book
crying	silky	sweet	smoky	bitter
salty	skunk	cold	smooth	stinky

Touch
silky
hot
cold
smooth

See
green
book
butterfly
rainbow

Taste
sweet
sour
salty
bitter

Smell
stinky
smoky
moldy
skunk

Hear
music
crying
talking
honking

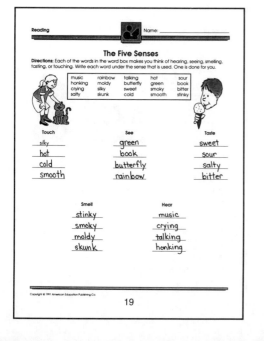

Review

Directions: Put a check in the box by the three words that belong together. Then draw a line under the sentence that tells how they are alike.

1. ✓forehead ✓jaw — They are all parts of the face.
   ☐ shoulder ✓cheek — They are all parts of the arm.

2. ✓collar ✓sleeve — They are all parts of a your body.
   ✓cuff ☐ heart — They are all parts of a shirt.

3. ☐ camera ✓trumpet — They are all used to make music.
   ✓guitar ✓flute — They are all used to take pictures.

Directions: Check the three words that belong together. Then write a sentence to tell how they are alike.

✓cottage ☐ princess ✓hut ✓castle

sentences will vary

Directions: Write a word to complete each of the following analogies.

1. Car is to drive as — plane — is to fly.
2. Basement is to bottom as attic is to — top
3. Calf is to cow as colt is to — horse
4. Bark is to dog as — moo — is to cow.

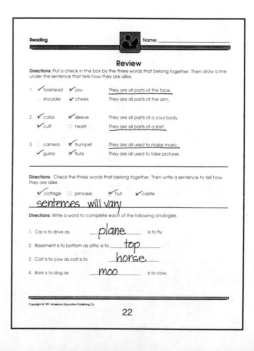

Understanding Newspaper Ads

Directions: Use the following newspaper ad to answer the questions.

House of Plants
Colorful Flowering Trees

Flowering Crab Apple Trees
Sizes up to 10 ft.
Beautiful Colored Spring Flowers
Dark Green Foliage
Red, Pink, White Blossoms

25% OFF

Reg. $29.99 to $149.99
NOW $22.49 to $112.50

House of Plants
6280 River Road 29539

1. How big are the biggest flowering crab apple trees for sale? **10 ft.**

2. What are the regular prices? **$29.99 to $149.99**

3. What are the sale prices? **$22.49 to $112.50**

The Solar System

You live on a planet — the planet Earth. It is one of nine planets that follows an **orbit** around the sun. The other eight planets are Mercury, Venus, Mars, Jupiter, Saturn, Uranus, Neptune, and Pluto. These nine planets are part of the solar system. The word sol, the base word for solar, means sun. The sun is at the center of the solar system and is the most important part. So, you could call the solar system the sun system.

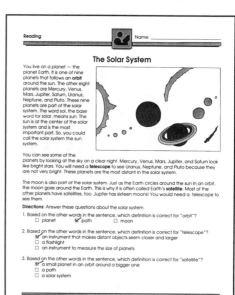

You can see some of the planets by looking at the sky on a clear night. Mercury, Venus, Mars, Jupiter, and Saturn look like bright stars. You will need a **telescope** to see Uranus, Neptune, and Pluto because they are not very bright. These planets are the most distant in the solar system.

The moon is also part of the solar system. Just as the Earth circles around the sun in an orbit, the moon goes around the Earth. This is why it is often called Earth's **satellite**. Some of the other planets have satellites, too. Jupiter has sixteen moons! You would need a telescope to see them.

Directions: Answer these questions about the solar system.

1. Based on the other words in the sentence, which definition is correct for "orbit"?
   ☐ planet   ☑ path   ☐ moon

2. Based on the other words in the sentence, which definition is correct for "telescope"?
   ☑ an instrument that makes distant objects seem closer and larger
   ☐ a flashlight
   ☐ an instrument to measure the size of planets

3. Based on the other words in the sentence, which definition is correct for "satelite"?
   ☑ a small planet in an orbit around a bigger one
   ☐ a path
   ☐ a solar system

Reading A Train Schedule

Directions: Below is part of a schedule for trains leaving New York City for cities all around the country. Use the schedule to answer the questions.

Destination	Train Number	Departure Time	Arrival Time
Birmingham	958	9:00 a.m.	12:31 a.m.
Boston	611	7:15 a.m.	4:30 p.m.
Cambridge	398	8:15 a.m.	1:14 p.m.
Cincinnati	242	5:00 a.m.	7:25 p.m.
Detroit	415	1:45 p.m.	4:40 a.m.
Evansville	623	3:00 p.m.	8:28 a.m.

1. What is the number of the train that leaves latest in the day? **623**

2. What city is the destination for train #623? **Evansville**

3. What time does the train for Boston leave New York? **7:15 a.m.**

4. What time does train #415 arrive in Detroit? **4:40 a.m.**

5. What is the destination of the train that leaves earliest in the day? **Cincinnati**

Planet Facts

It takes Earth 365 days — one year — to complete one orbit around the sun. Mercury, the planet closest to the sun, takes only 88 days to orbit the sun. But Pluto takes about 248 years!

Because they are the farthest from the sun, Neptune and Pluto are the coldest planets. Their temperatures are about 320 degrees below zero! Mercury and Venus are the hottest planets. The temperature can reach 600 degrees on Mercury and 860 degrees on Venus. Plants and animals cannot live on these planets because they would either freeze or burn up. In fact, scientists believe that Earth is the only planet in our solar system where plants, animals, and people can live. This is why Earth is called the "Life Planet."

Earth is a middle-sized planet. Four of the planets are smaller than Earth. They are Mercury, Venus, Mars, and Pluto. Jupiter, Saturn, Uranus, and Neptune are all larger than Earth. Jupiter is the biggest planet. It is more than 1,000 times bigger than Earth. Pluto is the smallest planet. Earth is about four times bigger than Pluto.

The sun is really a star. Stars are balls of hot, glowing gas. The sun looks so much bigger than the other stars because it is so much closer. It is only 93 million miles away from the Earth. The next closest star is 25 trillion miles away!

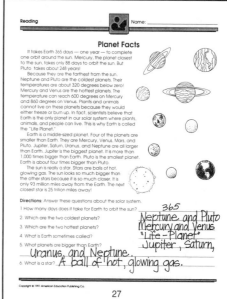

Directions: Answer these questions about the solar system.

1. How many days does it take for Earth to orbit the sun? **365**

2. Which are the two coldest planets? **Neptune and Pluto**

3. Which are the two hottest planets? **Mercury and Venus**

4. What is Earth sometimes called? **"Life-Planet"**

5. What planets are bigger than Earth? **Jupiter, Saturn, Uranus, and Neptune.**

6. What is a star? **A ball of hot, glowing gas.**

Hummingbirds

Hummingbirds are the smallest birds in the world. But this tiny bird is quite an acrobat. Only a few birds, such as kingfishers and sunbirds, can hover, which means to stay in one place in the air. But no other bird can match the flying skills of the hummingbird. The hummingbird can hover, fly backward, and fly upside down!

Hummingbirds get their name because their wings move very quickly when they fly. This causes a humming sound. Their wings move so fast that you can't see them at all. This takes a lot of energy. The hummingbird must have food about every 20 minutes to have enough strength to fly. Their favorite foods are insects and nectar. Nectar is the sweet water deep inside a flower. Hummingbirds use their long, thin bills to drink from the flowers. When a hummingbird sips nectar, it hovers in front of a flower. It never touches the flower with its wings or feet.

Besides being the best at flying, the hummingbird also is one of the prettiest birds. Of all the birds in the world, the hummingbird's colors are among the brightest. Some are bright green with red and white markings. Some are purple. One kind of hummingbird can change its color from reddish-brown to purple to red!

The hummingbird's nest is special, too. It looks like a tiny cup. The inside of the nest is very soft. This is because one of the things the mother bird uses to build the nest is the silk from a spider's web.

Directions: Answer these questions about hummingbirds.

1. Why do hummingbirds get their name?
   Because their wings hum when they fly.

2. What does hover mean?
   To stay in one place in the air.

3. How often do hummingbirds need to eat?
   Every 20 minutes

4. Name two things that hummingbirds eat.
   1) **insects**   2) **nectar**

5. What is one of the things a mother hummingbird uses to build her nest?
   Silk from a spider's web.

Mars Is Most Like Earth

Earth is the only planet that scientists are certain has life. What does Earth have that the other planets don't? For one thing, Earth is just the right temperature. As the third planet from the sun, earth seems to be just the right distance away. The planets that are closer to the sun are so hot their surfaces are baking in the sun. The farthest planets are frozen balls.

When the Earth developed — which scientists believe may have happened about 4 billion years ago — many gases covered the earth. The gases caused the earth to be hot. But something wonderful happened. The temperature was just right for thick clouds to form. It rained very hard for a very long time. This gave Earth its oceans. Water made it possible for plants to grow. And the plants created oxygen in the atmosphere. Oxygen is the gas that humans and animals breathe.

Only one other planet in the solar system seems to be anything like ours is Mars. That planet is Mars. Mars is smaller than Earth, and it is quite a bit cooler. But it is not too cold for humans. On some days, the temperatures are as cold as a winter day in the northern United States. If you wore a special space suit, you could walk around on Mars. You would have to bring your own air to breathe, though. The air on Mars is too thin to breathe.

Mars has the largest volcano in the solar system. It is sixteen miles high. The highest volcano on Earth is five miles high. The most unexpected sight on Mars is dried-up river beds. Scientists believe that Mars was once much wetter. Does this mean there could have been living things on Mars? Scientists are not sure, but there has been no sign so far.

Directions: Answer these questions about Mars and Earth.

1. Name three things that Earth has that makes life possible.
   1) **temperature**   2) **water**   3) **oxygen**

2. According to scientists, how long ago did Earth develop? **4 billion years**

3. What planet is most like Earth? **Mars**

4. Mars has the biggest volcano in the solar system. How tall is it? **16 miles**

5. Why couldn't you breathe on Mars? **The air is too thin.**

The Moon

Earth has a partner in its trip around the sun. It is the moon. The moon is the Earth's satellite. It moves around the Earth very quickly. It takes the moon 28 days to go around the Earth one time.

While they are partners in the solar system, the Earth and the moon are very different. The Earth is filled with life. It is a very colorful planet. The moon is gray and lifeless. Nothing can live on the moon.

There is no air on the moon. Astronauts must wear special space suits when they walk on the moon so they can breathe. The moon also has no water. And there is no weather, so the sky above the moon always looks black.

You would not weigh as much on the moon as you do on Earth. If you weigh 100 pounds, you would weigh only 16 pounds on the moon. It is very different to walk on the moon, too. You would bounce and float!

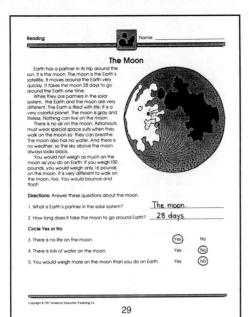

Directions: Answer these questions about the moon.

1. What is Earth's partner in the solar system?   The moon.

2. How long does it take the moon to go around Earth?   28 days.

Circle Yes or No

3. There is no life on the moon.   (Yes)   No

4. There is lots of water on the moon.   Yes   (No)

5. You would weigh more on the moon than you do on Earth.   Yes   (No)

Your Five Senses

Your senses are very important to you. You depend on them every day. They tell you where you are and what is going on around you. Your senses are sight, hearing, touch, smell, and taste.

Try to imagine for a minute that you were suddenly unable to use your senses. Imagine, for instance, that you are in a cave and your only source of light is a candle. Without warning, a gust of wind blows out the flame.

This might not be a very pleasant thought, but it helps to show how you depend on your senses. They are always at work. Your eyes let you read this book. Your nose brings the scent of dinner cooking. Your hand feels the softness as you stroke a puppy. Your ears tell you that a storm is approaching.

Your senses also help to keep you from harm. They warn you if you touch something that will burn you. They keep you from looking at a light that is too bright, and they tell you if a car is coming up behind you. Each of your senses collects information and sends it as a message to your brain. The brain is like the control center for your body. It sorts out the messages sent by your senses and acts on them.

Directions: Answer these questions about the five senses.

1. The main idea is:

   Your senses keep you from harm.

   (Your senses are important to you in many ways.)

2. Name the five senses.

   1) sight   2) hearing   3) smell

   4) touch   5) taste

3. Which part of your body acts as the "control center"?   The brain.

Review

The volcano is one of the most amazing and frightening forces of nature. Maybe you have seen pictures of these "fireworks" of nature. Sometimes when a volcano **erupts**, a huge wall of melted rock creeps down the side of a mountain. It looks like a "river of fire." Sometimes volcanoes explode, throwing the melted rock and ashes high into the air. But where does this melted rock come from?

The earth is made up of many **layers**. The top layer that we see is called the crust. Under the crust are many layers of hard rock. But far, far beneath the crust is rock so hot that it is soft. In some places it even melts. The melted rock is called magma. Sometimes the magma breaks out to the surface through cracks in the crust. These cracks are volcanoes.

Most people think of mountains when they think of volcanoes. But not every mountain is a volcano. A volcano is simply the opening in the earth from which the magma escapes. The hot magma, or lava as it is called, cools and builds up on the surface of the earth. Over thousands of years, this pile of cooled lava can grow to be very, very big. For example, the highest mountain in Africa, Kilimanjaro, is a volcano. It towers more than 16,000 feet above the ground around it.

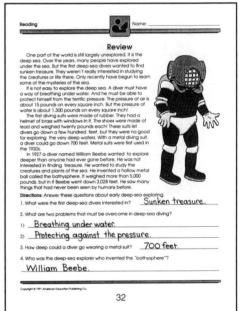

Directions: Answer these questions about volcanoes.

1. Based on the context of the other words in the sentence, what is the correct definition of the word "erupts"?
   ☐ drips out   ☑ bursts out   ☐ seals up

2. Based on the context of the other words in the sentence, what is the correct definition of the word "layer"?
   ☐ rocks   ☑ a single thickness   ☐ ground

3. What is the top layer of the earth called?   crust

4. What is the word for hot magma that spills out of the earth?   lava

5. Where is the volcano called Kilimanjaro located?   Africa

Review

One part of the world is still largely unexplored. It is the deep sea. Over the years, many people have explored under the sea. But the first deep-sea divers wanted to find sunken treasure. They weren't really interested in studying the creatures or life there. Only recently have people begun to learn some of the mysteries of the sea.

It is not easy to explore the deep sea. A diver must have a way of breathing under water. And he must be able to protect himself from the terrific pressure. The pressure of air is about 15 pounds on every square inch. But the pressure of water is about 1,300 pounds on every square inch!

The first diving suits were made of rubber. They had a helmet of brass with windows in it. The shoes were made of lead and weighed twenty pounds each! These suits let divers go down a few hundred feet, but they were no good for exploring the very deep waters. With a metal diving suit, a diver could go down 700 feet. Metal suits were first used in the 1930s.

In 1927 a diver named William Beebe wanted to explore deeper than anyone had ever gone before. He was not interested in finding treasure. He wanted to study the creatures and plants of the sea. He invented a hollow metal ball called the bathysphere. It weighed more than 5,000 pounds, but in it Beebe went down 3,028 feet. He saw many things that had never been seen by humans before.

Directions: Answer these questions about early deep-sea exploring.

1. What were the first deep-sea divers interested in?   Sunken treasure.

2. What are two problems that must be overcome in deep-sea diving?

   1) Breathing under water.

   2) Protecting against the pressure.

3. How deep could a diver go wearing a metal suit?   700 feet.

4. Who was the deep-sea explorer who invented the "bathysphere"?

   William Beebe.

Notes

Notes

Review

Here's a science experiment that you can do in your own backyard. To make this "rocket launcher," you will need an empty one-quart soda bottle, a cork, a paper towel, a half cup of water, a half cup of vinegar, and one teaspoon of baking soda. You may want to add some streamers.

The cork will be the "rocket." If you attach tissue-paper streamers to the cork with a thumbtack, you will be able to more easily follow the rocket during its flight.

Pour the water and vinegar into the "launcher" — the bottle. Cut the paper towel into a four-inch square. Put the baking soda into the middle of the paper towel. Roll up the towel and twist the ends so the baking soda will stay inside.

Outside, where there will be plenty of room for your rocket to fly, drop the paper towel and the baking soda into the bottle. Put the cork on as tightly as you can.

The liquid will soak through the paper towel. This lets the baking soda and vinegar work together to make a kind of gas called carbon dioxide. As the carbon dioxide builds up in the bottle, it will push out the cork. Soon the cork will shoot up to the sky with a loud pop!

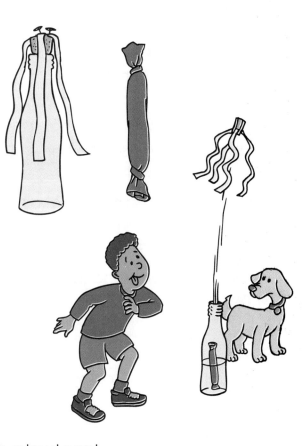

Directions: After reading about how to make a "rocket launcher," number in order the steps.

_____ Pour the vinegar and water into the soda bottle.

_____ Attach streamers to the cork so you can follow its flight.

_____ Stand back and watch for your "rocket" to blast off!

_____ Put the baking soda on the paper towel and roll it up.

_____ Wait as the vinegar and baking soda work to make carbon dioxide gas.

_____ Drop the paper towel with the baking soda into the bottle.

_____ Gather together a bottle, cork, water, vinegar, paper towel, and baking soda.

_____ Put on the cork as tightly as you can.

Name: _____

Which One Does Not Belong?

Directions: For each one, cross out the word that does not belong with the others.

1. Cross out the word that is not a building.

   factory   hotel   lodge   pattern

2. Cross out the word that is not a month.

   Thursday   September   December   October

3. Cross out the word that is not a place where people live.

   cottage   hut   carpenter   castle

4. Cross out the word that is not found in a kitchen.

   cupboard   orchard   refrigerator   stove

5. Cross out the word that is not a holiday.

   Christmas   Thanksgiving   Easter   spring

6. Cross out the word that is not a kind of metal.

   brass   copper   coal   tin

7. Cross out the word that is not a part of the body.

   stomach   breathe   liver   brain

8. Cross out the word that is not a person.

   teacher   mother   dentist   office

9. Cross out the word that is not found in a bathroom.

   musket   faucet   bathtub   sink

10. Cross out the word that is not an area of a house.

    basement   attic   kitchen   neighborhood

Name: _____

Classifying: The Five Senses

Directions: Each of the words in the word box makes you think of hearing, seeing, smelling, tasting, or touching. Write each word under the sense that is used. One is done for you.

music	rainbow	talking	hot	sour
honking	moldy	butterfly	green	book
crying	silky	sweet	smoky	bitter
salty	skunk	cold	smooth	stinky

Touch

silky

_____

_____

_____

_____

See

_____

_____

_____

_____

Taste

_____

_____

_____

_____

Smell

_____

_____

_____

_____

Hear

_____

_____

_____

_____

Name: _____

Analogies: Relating Things

Directions: Write a word from the word box to complete the following analogies. One is done for you.

cut	carry	ran	arm	listen
paint	lie	children	fifty	out
puppy	summer	hot	water	egg

1. Pencil is to write as brush is to _____paint_____ .

2. Foot is to leg as hand is to _____ .

3. Crayons are to draw as scissors are to _____ .

4. Leg is to walk as arm is to _____ .

5. Baby is to babies as child is to _____ .

6. Eye is to look as ear is to _____ .

7. Chair is to sit as bed is to _____ .

8. 600 is to 300 as 100 is to _____ .

9. White is to black as in is to _____ .

10. Ice skate is to winter as swim is to _____ .

11. Switch is to light as faucet is to _____ .

12. Fly is to flew as run is to _____ .

13. Cow is to milk as chicken is to _____ .

14. Cool is to cold as warm is to _____ .

15. Cat is to kitten as dog is to _____ .

Name: _____

Analogies: What Fits Best

Directions: For each analogy, write a word from the word box that best fits.

fence	club	glove	saw	father
blanket	dish	rug	snow	ten
compass	hat	brake	finger	blue

1. Racket is to tennis as _____ is to golf.

2. Glass is to drink as _____ is to eat.

3. Wheel is to steer as _____ is to stop.

4. Roof is to house as _____ is to floor.

5. Rain is to storm as _____ is to blizzard.

6. Clock is to time as _____ is to directions.

7. Lid is to pan as _____ is to head.

8. Hammer is to pound as _____ is to cut.

9. Mother is to daughter as _____ is to son.

10. Shoe is to foot as _____ is to hand.

11. Five is to ten as _____ is to twenty.

12. Shade is to lamp as _____ is to bed.

13. Toe is to foot as _____ is to hand.

14. Frame is to picture as _____ is to yard.

15. Green is to grass as _____ is to sky.

Name: _____

Review

Directions: Put a check in the box by the three words that belong together. Then draw a line under the sentence that tells how they are alike.

1. ☐ forehead   ☐ jaw   They are all parts of the face.

    ☐ shoulder   ☐ cheek   They are all parts of the arm.

2. ☐ collar   ☐ sleeve   They are all parts of a your body.

    ☐ cuff   ☐ heart   They are all parts of a shirt.

3. ☐ camera   ☐ trumpet   They are all used to make music.

    ☐ guitar   ☐ flute   They are all used to take pictures.

Directions: Check the three words that belong together. Then write a sentence to tell how they are alike.

☐ cottage   ☐ princess   ☐ hut   ☐ castle

Directions: Write a word to complete each of the following analogies.

1. Car is to drive as _____ is to fly.

2. Basement is to bottom as attic is to _____ .

3. Calf is to cow as colt is to _____ .

4. Bark is to dog as _____ is to cow.

Name: _____

Practical Reading Skills: Newspaper Ads

Directions: Use the following newspaper ad to answer the questions.

House of Plants

Colorful Flowering Trees

Flowering Crab Apple Trees
Sizes up to 10 ft.
Beautiful Colored Spring Flowers
Dark Green Foliage
Red, Pink, White Blossoms

25% OFF

Reg. $29.99 to $149.99
NOW $22.49 to $112.50

House of Plants
6280 River Road 29539

1. How big are the biggest flowering
   crab apple trees for sale?   _____

2. What are the regular prices?   _____

3. What are the sale prices?   _____

Name: _____

Practical Reading Skills: Train Schedule

Directions: Below is part of a schedule for trains leaving New York City for cities all around the country. Use the schedule to answer the questions.

Destination	Train Number	Departure Time	Arrival Time
Birmingham	958	9:00 a.m.	12:31a.m.
Boston	611	7:15 a.m.	4:30 p.m.
Cambridge	398	8:15 a.m.	1:14 p.m.
Cincinnati	242	5:00 a.m.	7:25 p.m.
Detroit	415	1:45 p.m.	4:40 a.m.
Evansville	623	3:00 p.m.	8:28 a.m.

1. What is the number of the train that leaves latest in the day? _____

2. What city is the destination for train #623? _____

3. What time does the train for Boston leave New York? _____

4. What time does train #415 arrive in Detroit? _____

5. What is the destination of the train that leaves earliest in the day? _____

Name: _____

Recognizing Details: Hummingbirds

Hummingbirds are the smallest birds in the world. But this tiny bird is quite an acrobat. Only a few birds, such as kingfishers and sunbirds, can hover, which means to stay in one place in the air. But no other bird can match the flying skills of the hummingbird. The hummingbird can hover, fly backward, and fly upside down!

Hummingbirds get their name because their wings move very quickly when they fly. This causes a humming sound. Their wings move so fast that you can't see them at all. This takes a lot of energy. These little birds must have food about every 20 minutes to have enough strength to fly. Their favorite foods are insects and nectar. Nectar is the sweet water deep inside a flower. Hummingbirds use their long, thin bills to drink from the flowers. When a hummingbird sips nectar, it hovers in front of a flower. It never touches the flower with its wings or feet.

Besides being the best at flying, the hummingbird also is one of the prettiest birds. Of all the birds in the world, the hummingbird's colors are among the brightest. Some are bright green with red and white markings. Some are purple. One kind of hummingbird can change its color from reddish-brown to purple to red!

The hummingbird's nest is special, too. It looks like a tiny cup. The inside of the nest is very soft. This is because one of the things the mother bird uses to build the nest is the silk from a spider's web.

Directions: Answer these questions about hummingbirds.

1. Why did hummingbirds get their name?

_____

2. What does hover mean?

_____

3. How often do hummingbirds need to eat?

_____

4. Name two things that hummingbirds eat.

1) _____   2) _____

5. What is one of the things a mother hummingbird uses to build her nest?

_____

Name: _____

Context: The Solar System

You live on a planet — the planet Earth. It is one of nine planets that follows an **orbit** around the sun. The other eight planets are Mercury, Venus, Mars, Jupiter, Saturn, Uranus, Neptune, and Pluto. These nine planets are part of the solar system. The word sol, the base word for solar, means sun. The sun is at the center of the solar system and is the most important part. So, you could call the solar system the sun system.

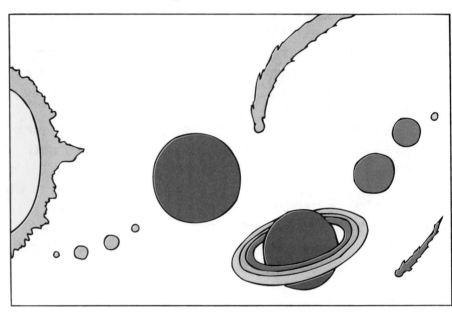

You can see some of the planets by looking at the sky on a clear night. Mercury, Venus, Mars, Jupiter, and Saturn look like bright stars. You will need a **telescope** to see Uranus, Neptune, and Pluto because they are not very bright. These planets are the most distant in the solar system.

The moon is also part of the solar system. Just as the Earth circles around the sun in an orbit, the moon goes around the Earth. This is why it is often called Earth's **satellite**. Most of the other planets have satellites, too. Jupiter has sixteen moons! You would need a telescope to see them.

Directions: Answer these questions about the solar system.

1. Based on the other words in the sentence, which definition is correct for "orbit"?
   ☐ planet   ☐ path   ☐ moon

2. Based on the other words in the sentence, which definition is correct for "telescope"?
   ☐ an instrument that makes distant objects seem closer and larger
   ☐ a flashlight
   ☐ an instrument to measure the size of planets

3. Based on the other words in the sentence, which definition is correct for "satellite"?
   ☐ a small heavenly body in an orbit around a bigger one
   ☐ a path
   ☐ a solar system

Name: _____

Recognizing Details: Planet Facts

It takes Earth 365 days — one year — to complete one orbit around the sun. Mercury, the planet closest to the sun, takes only 88 days to orbit the sun. But Pluto takes about 248 years!

Because they are the farthest from the sun, Neptune and Pluto are the coldest planets. Their temperatures are about 320 degrees below zero! Mercury and Venus are the hottest planets. The temperature can reach 600 degrees on Mercury and 860 degrees on Venus. Plants and animals cannot live on these planets because they would either freeze or burn up. In fact, scientists believe that Earth is the only planet in our solar system where plants, animals, and people can live. This is why Earth is called the "Life Planet."

Earth is a middle-sized planet. Four of the planets are smaller than Earth. They are Mercury, Venus, Mars, and Pluto. Jupiter, Saturn, Uranus, and Neptune are all larger than Earth. Jupiter is the biggest planet. It is more than 1,000 times bigger than Earth. Pluto is the smallest planet. Earth is about four times bigger than Pluto.

The sun is really a star. Stars are balls of hot, glowing gas. The sun looks so much bigger than the other stars because it is so much closer. It is only 93 million miles away from the Earth. The next closest star is 25 trillion miles away!

Directions: Answer these questions about the solar system.

1 How many days does it take for Earth to orbit the sun? _____

2. Which are the two coldest planets? _____

3. Which are the two hottest planets? _____

4. What is Earth sometimes called? _____

5. What planets are bigger than Earth? _____

_____

6. What is a star? _____

Name: _____

Recognizing Details: Mars Is Most Like Earth

Earth is the only planet that scientists are certain has life. What does Earth have that the other planets don't? For one thing, Earth is just the right temperature. As the third planet from the sun, earth seems to be just the right distance away. The planets that are closer to the sun are so hot their surfaces are baking in the sun. The farthest planets are frozen balls.

When the Earth developed — which scientists believe may have happened about 4 billion years ago — many gases covered the earth. The gases caused the Earth to be hot. But something wonderful happened. The temperature was just right for thick clouds to form. It rained very hard for a very long time. This gave Earth its oceans. Water made it possible for plants to grow. The plants created oxygen in the atmosphere. Oxygen is the gas that humans and animals breathe.

Only one other planet in the solar system seems to be anything like Earth. That planet is Mars. Mars is smaller than Earth, and it is quite a bit cooler. But it is not too cold for humans. On some days, the temperatures are as cold as a winter day in the northern United States. If you wore a special space suit, you could walk around on Mars. You would have to bring your own air to breathe, though. The air on Mars is too thin to breathe.

Mars has the largest volcano in the solar system. It is sixteen miles high. The highest volcano on Earth is five miles high. The most unexpected sight on Mars is dried-up river beds. Scientists believe that Mars was once much wetter. Does this mean there could have been living things on Mars? Scientists are not sure, but there has been no sign so far.

Directions: Answer these questions about Mars and Earth.

1. Name three things that Earth has that makes life possible.

1) _____ 2) _____ 3) _____

2. According to scientists, how long ago did Earth develop? _____

3. What planet is most like Earth? _____

4. Mars has the biggest volcano in the solar system. How tall is it? _____

5. Why couldn't you breathe on Mars? _____

Name: _____

Remembering What You Read: The Moon

Earth has a partner in its trip around the sun. It is the moon. The moon is the Earth's satellite. It moves around the Earth very quickly. It takes the moon 28 days to go around the Earth one time.

While they are partners in the solar system, the Earth and the moon are very different. The Earth is filled with life. It is a very colorful planet. The moon is gray and lifeless. Nothing can live on the moon.

There is no air on the moon. Astronauts must wear special space suits when they walk on the moon so they can breathe. The moon also has no water. There is no weather, so the sky above the moon always looks black.

You would not weigh as much on the moon as you do on Earth. If you weigh 100 pounds, you would weigh only 16 pounds on the moon. It is very different to walk on the moon, too. You would bounce and float!

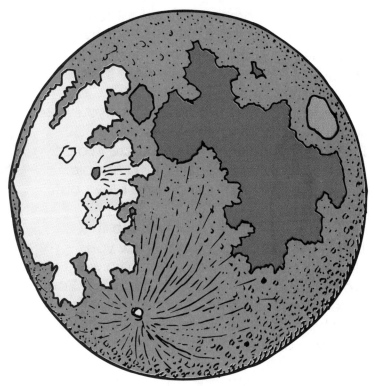

Directions: Answer these questions about the moon.

1. What is Earth's partner in the solar system? _____

2. How long does it take the moon to go around Earth? _____

Circle Yes or No

3. There is no life on the moon.   Yes   No

4. There is lots of water on the moon.   Yes   No

5. You would weigh more on the moon than you do on Earth. Yes   No

Name: _____

Main Idea: Your Five Senses

Your senses are very important to you. You depend on them every day. They tell you where you are and what is going on around you. Your senses are sight, hearing, touch, smell, and taste.

Try to imagine for a minute that you were suddenly unable to use your senses. Imagine, for instance, that you are in a cave and your only source of light is a candle. Without warning, a gust of wind blows out the flame.

This might not be a very pleasant thought, but it helps to show how you depend on your senses. They are always at work. Your eyes let you read this book. Your nose brings the scent of dinner cooking. Your hand feels the softness as you stroke a puppy. Your ears tell you that a storm is approaching.

Your senses also help to keep you from harm. They warn you if you touch something that will burn you. They keep you from looking at a light that is too bright, and they tell you if a car is coming up behind you. Each of your senses collects information and sends it as a message to your brain. The brain is like the control center for your body. It sorts out the messages sent by your senses and acts on them.

Directions: Answer these questions about the five senses.

1. The main idea is:

    Your senses keep you from harm.

    Your senses are important to you in many ways.

2. Name the five senses.

1)_____ 2) _____ 3) _____

4)_____ 5) _____

3. Which part of your body acts as the "control center"? _____

Name: _____

Review

The volcano is one of the most amazing and frightening forces of nature. Maybe you have seen pictures of these "fireworks" of nature. Sometimes when a volcano **erupts**, a huge wall of melted rock creeps down the side of a mountain. It looks like a "river of fire." Sometimes volcanoes explode, throwing the melted rock and ashes high into the air. But where does this melted rock come from?

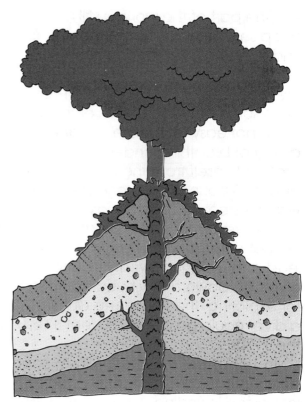

The earth is made up of many **layers**. The top layer that we see is called the crust. Under the crust are many layers of hard rock. But far, far beneath the crust is rock so hot that it is soft. In some places it even melts. The melted rock is called magma. Sometimes the magma breaks out to the surface through cracks in the crust. These cracks are volcanoes.

Most people think of mountains when they think of volcanoes. But not every mountain is a volcano. A volcano is simply the opening in the earth from which the magma escapes. The hot magma, or lava as it is called, cools and builds up on the surface of the earth. Over thousands of years, this pile of cooled lava can grow to be very, very big. For example, the highest mountain in Africa, Kilimanjaro, is a volcano. It towers more than 16,000 feet above the ground around it.

Directions: Answer these questions about volcanoes.

1. Based on the context of the other words in the sentence, what is the correct definition of the word "erupts"?

 ☐ drips out ☐ bursts out ☐ seals up

2. Based on the context of the other words in the sentence, what is the correct definition of the word "layer"?

 ☐ rocks ☐ a single thickness ☐ ground

3. What is the top layer of the earth called? _____

4. What is the word for hot magma that spills out of the earth? _____

5. Where is the volcano called Kilimanjaro located? _____

Name: _____

Review

One part of the world is still largely unexplored. It is the deep sea. Over the years, many people have explored under the sea. But the first deep-sea divers wanted to find sunken treasure. They weren't really interested in studying the creatures of life there. Only recently have they begun to learn some of the mysteries of the sea.

Its not easy to explore the deep sea. A diver must have a way of breathing under water. He must be able to protect himself from the terrific pressure. The pressure of air is about 15 pounds on every square inch. But the pressure of water is about 1,300 pounds on every square inch!

The first diving suits were made of rubber. They had a helmet of brass with windows in it. The shoes were made of lead and weighed twenty pounds each! These suits let divers go down a few hundred feet, but they were no good for exploring the very deep waters. With a metal diving suit, a diver could go down 700 feet. Metal suits were first used in the 1930s.

In 1927 a diver named William Beebe wanted to explore deeper than anyone had ever gone before. He was not interested in finding treasure. He wanted to study the creatures and plants of the sea. He invented a hollow metal ball called the bathysphere. It weighed more than 5,000 pounds, but in it Beebe went down 3,028 feet. He saw many things that had never been seen by humans before.

Directions: Answer these questions about early deep-sea exploring.

1. What were the first deep-sea divers interested in? _____

2. What are two problems that must be overcome in deep-sea diving?

1) _____

2) _____

3. How deep could a diver go wearing a metal suit? _____

4. Who was the deep-sea explorer who invented the "bathysphere"?

_____